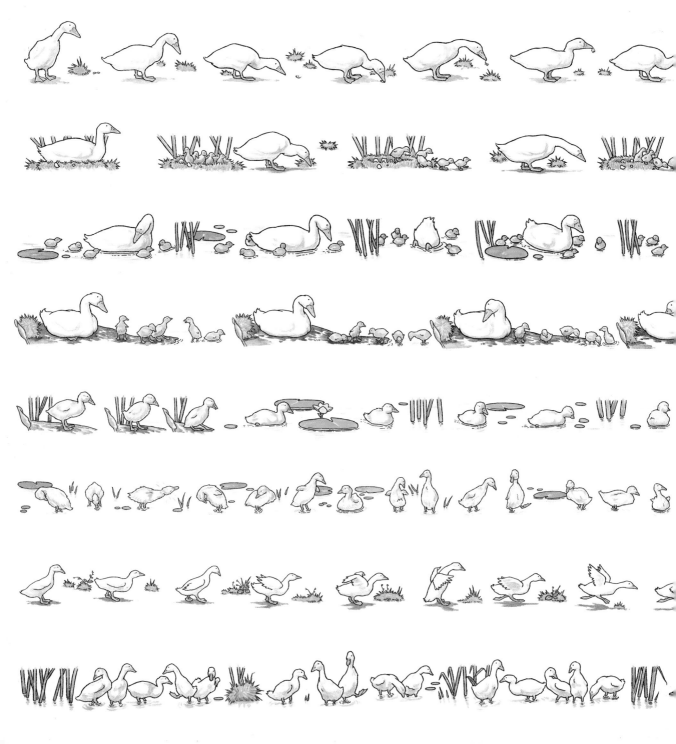

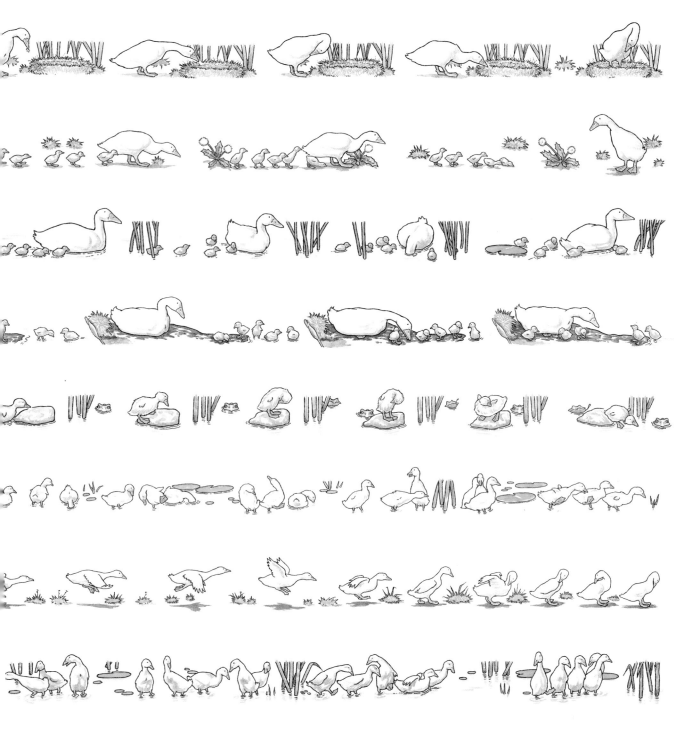

Dorling **DK** Kindersley

LONDON, NEW YORK, SYDNEY, DELHI, PARIS, MUNICH, AND JOHANNESBURG

Written and edited by Angela Royston
Art Editor Nigel Hazle
Production Marguerite Fenn
Illustrator Rowan Clifford

First American Edition, 2001

00 01 02 03 04 05 10 9 8 7 6 5 4 3 2 1

Published in the United States by Dorling Kindersley Publishing, Inc.
95 Madison Avenue, New York, New York 10016

A CIP catalog record for this book is available
from the Library of Congress

ISBN 0-7894-7655-X

Color reproduction by Scantrans, Singapore
Printed and bound in Italy by L.E.G.O.

See our complete
catalog at

www.dk.com

SEE HOW THEY GROW

DUCK

photographed by
BARRIE WATTS

A DORLING KINDERSLEY BOOK

In the nest

My mother has laid her eggs in this
nest. She sits on them to keep
them warm.

Inside each egg a new duckling
is growing. This one is me. I am
just beginning to hatch.

Just hatched

I have chipped
away my shell
and now I am
pushing myself out.

At last I am out of my egg.

I can see and hear and stand and walk. I can cheep too. Where is my mother?

9

First swim

I am two days old now. I am going to the pond for my first swim.

As soon as I am in the water, I start to swim.

I use my webbed feet to push me through the water.

Feeding

I am seven days old and getting bigger. I like to explore new things.

This bowl has wet mud in it.
I search the mud with my
beak for things to eat.

Now I've jumped right into the bowl.

In the water

I dabble in the water for things to eat.

I am two weeks old and I love to swim in the water.

I shake the water off my feathers.

New feathers

I am three weeks old.
My yellow down is
falling out and new
white feathers are
beginning to grow.

I stay close to the other ducklings.
Our mother watches out for danger.

Sometimes we huddle together. Our fuzzy feathers help to keep us warm.

Nearly grown up

I am six weeks old and
nearly grown up.

18

All my feathers are white and my wings are bigger and stronger.

See how much I have grown. This bowl is small now, but it seemed big when I first jumped into it.

See how I grew

The egg

One hour old

Two days old

Seven days old

Two weeks old

Three weeks old   Six weeks old

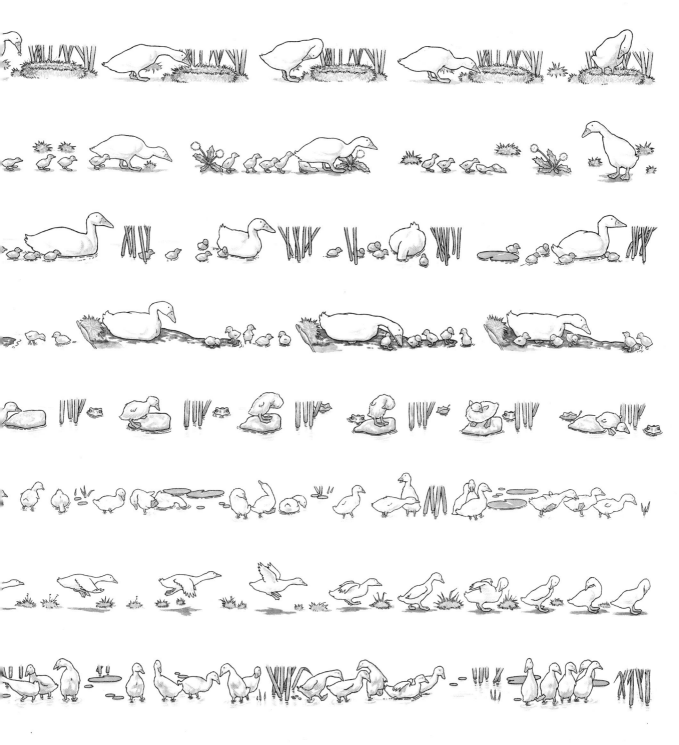